Stefanie (Gig) Sixsmith grew up in Surrey, graduating with a degree in Graphic Design from Kingston School of Art. She launched her design career with Virgin Atlantic, followed by 30 years of independent commercial design work.

Inspired by her daughters, when they were young, she designed a range of children's educational products, which she uses to run imagination workshops in schools – www.imagineocean.uk

Stefanie's talent gave her the vision to create and share this emotional journey following her experience with breast cancer.

She lives in Warwickshire with her husband, teenage daughters and their black Labrador, and goes by her childhood nickname Gig.

dp

1932-2016

For my dad,
who had wisdom beyond bounds
and taught me more than I can say.
Always in my heart.

Stefanie Sixsmith

SEE THE COLOUR IN THE CLOUDS

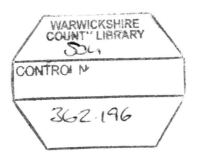
AUSTIN MACAULEY PUBLISHERS™

LONDON * CAMBRIDGE * NEW YORK * SHARJAH

A CIP catalogue record for this title is available from the British Library.

ISBN 9781528999977 (Paperback)
ISBN 9781786297785 (ePub e-book)

www.austinmacauley.com

First Published 2021
Austin Macauley Publishers Ltd®
1 Canada Square
Canary Wharf
London
E14 5AA

Thank you to our friends and family.

You helped us so much, both emotionally and logistically. Taking care of the girls, helping us to move house, collecting the girls from school at very short notice, sending me books to read, even telling me I looked fab in the school playground, when I'm quite sure I in fact didn't!

Thank you all for listening, for respecting our feelings and keeping things as normal as possible, especially a sense of humour. Thank you for the hearty soup – you know who you are!

Thank you to everyone at UHCW and The Arden Centre, for your big hearts, your dedication, your long hours and for the friendship and respect that you give to all your patients.

Thank you Mum and Dad for being there and staying strong for me, especially as Mum knew first-hand the fear of facing up to treatment.

Thank you to my Ian for staying focussed and strong, and holding my hand along the way.

And thank you especially to my girls, for your unquestioning tenderness and love. You filled my heart with your magic and gave me new strength every day.

Front cover image: The Clouds Crying

This painting always spoke to me:

The clouds – some angry, some hopeful, tears of joy and tears of pain. The wet summer of 2012 with its clouds forever crying. The scan-like shadows of threatening clouds lurking behind colourful clouds. The idea of veins and blood. And of course, the chemo drugs dripping slowly down through the tube to do their work.

Original painting by my daughter Lulu.

A uniquely artistic addition to the burgeoning survivorship literature which should be mandatory reading for all professionally involved with cancer care. Insightful and sincere, this engaging mix of reflections, told through words and graphics from a patient's perspective, will also help other patients realise they are not alone in their journey.

Christopher J Poole, Consultant Medical Oncologist

Having kept a diary, since I became pregnant with my first daughter in 2004, it was no surprise that I turned to my diary for comfort when I was diagnosed in 2012 with breast cancer.

Being a graphic artist, imagery played a huge part in my diaries and helped me to express my feelings. My world had been turned upside down. It's not hard to imagine that such a trauma – a question mark lurking over your existence, your future – is going to have a huge emotional impact. As many others have said, you never quite resume your former self – your pre-cancer persona.

The very best advice I had from a good friend was to not allow cancer to rule me. I didn't understand the significance of this until much later. I learned some important lessons throughout my journey; I cherished life and I yearned for it instead of taking it for granted, I was able to see the things that were really precious and I ignored the superficial. I definitely view life differently today.

The love and support that I had from my daughters, my husband, Ian, our family and friends – who learned to let me do things 'my way', gave me the strength I needed.

Six years on, I revisited my diary and decided to share my words – in thoughts, feelings and visions – in the simple hope that they may prove to be thought-provoking and comforting to others.

From feelings of utter remoteness and fear to the discovery of laughter and comedy, I hope that there are moments that others can relate to whether they are facing this illness or supporting someone who is.

When it comes to cancer, everyone treads a unique path, and this is mine.

Questions.

After the shock of being diagnosed with breast cancer in 2012, I found myself wanting information and answers. Naturally I wanted to try to understand.

So much information,
So many statistics

I only once asked myself the question:

why me?

Looking back, there were really only two questions that I desperately wanted someone to answer for me:

Will I get through this?
Will I still be able to live a long life and see my daughters grow up?

And of course nobody could answer those questions.

The question mark seemed such a powerful symbol as I embarked on this journey
of uncertainty.
I wanted to make a visual link between a question mark and the shape of the head and
neck, which is so curved once hair is gone.
Drawn on computer working from sketches in my diary.

Ultra Shock

The journey between doctor, breast consultant, scans and surgery was a swift and almost seamless step. The mammogram was not so much painful as really awkward – I never knew that a breast could stretch so far!

It was the ultrasound scan that scarred my memory deepest because it was at that point that I realised with complete certainty that all was not well.

A biopsy was performed there and then. They asked me if I wanted my husband with me, but my instinct was to say no; to delay this new reality from him for just a few more minutes while he was flicking through a newspaper in the waiting room.

I must have gone into a state of shock because I was suddenly so cold – and I couldn't stop shaking.

My husband did appear and I realised then just how much I needed him.

This image conveys the fear, vulnerability and shakiness that I felt during the ultrasound scan.
The composition centres on my left breast, whilst my head is lost, blurred and distorted.
Charcoal drawing, distorted on computer.

the Waiting Game . . .

The consultant spoke plainly to us and prepared us for what lay ahead; to be confirmed by the biopsy result.

An appointment was made for a week later.

Just a week to wait.
Just a week.

7 x 24 hours to wait.

(168 hrs)

Isn't time a strange concept. So elastic.

It holds events in place and yet it seems to vary so much, influenced by circumstances and emotions.

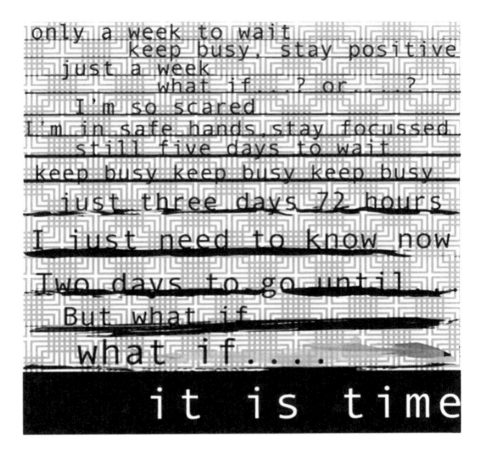

only a week to wait
         keep busy, stay positive
just a week
         what if...? or....?
I'm so scared
I'm in safe hands,stay focussed
   still five days to wait
keep busy keep busy keep busy
  just three days 72 hours
I just need to know now
Two days to go until
But what if
  what if....
                    it is time

The idea that life goes on and yet the voice inside my head is constantly speaking to me
as the clock ticks.
'It is time' – stark on its black background – the finality of the waiting time over
and it's time to face the verdict.
Image created on computer.

Staying Grounded

As I sit and write this diary, Lulu wanders in with all the worries of the world on her shoulders — she cannot find her little bag of earrings that she had for Christmas.

As I stare intently at my 8-year-old daughter – offering half-hearted suggestions of where to look for her earrings – it dawns on me just how wonderful childhood is, and how lucky I am to have my daughters to keep me grounded in reality throughout this otherwise daunting journey.

I became grateful for the everyday routines and confines of family life that kept everything moving forward and feeling as normal as possible.

I wanted this image to illustrate how my daughters kept me grounded in the real world.
They were sensitive and mature beyond their years. At times when I felt like floating
away, they would pull me back down to earth.
Using colour to represent the energy and life that the girls exuded, and the grey of the
heavy clouds above.
Mixed media.

Sibling Sense.

I hadn't planned to tell my brother so early on but he called me on the evening before my referral to the breast clinic and asked me very directly if I was OK? It seemed a funny question, unexpected under normal circumstances, but I felt I couldn't withhold the information once asked.

So I told him.

*He got the balance just right,
he seemed to know when to listen,
when to make me laugh
and when to swear!*

I guess when someone's known you all your life, they pick up vibes no matter how casual and normal you pretend to be.

He called and asked me one day if I'd design him a logo. Coincidentally my sister-in-law had also called that morning about a logo that she needed, and he said:

"Funny, isn't it, you get ill and everyone's getting their work orders in quick!"

It made me laugh all day.

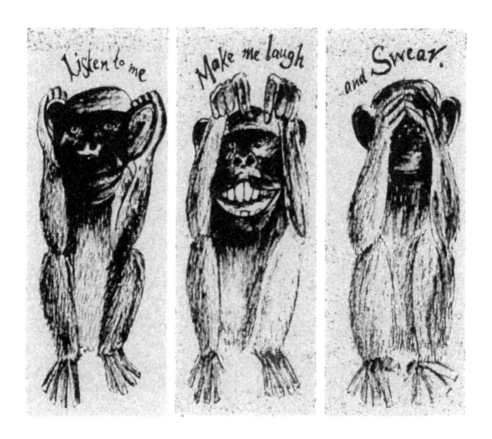

I used the idea of the three wise monkeys to express the balance that my brother had achieved in his dealing with the situation.
The 'prodding' fingers in the central monkey hark back to a time when as children we would prod each other and irritate each other by pretending that our fingers were antennae.
Created from a biro sketch.

Silent 'C'.

The appointment with the consultant was tense — it confirmed The dreaded C or silent C as I call it.

We were not surprised to hear the news – silent C now confirmed.

We vowed not to use the word to our daughters because we felt it could be upsetting for them if taken into the school playground and taken out of 'our' context.

Using this photo, I added the hopscotch as a way of placing cancer within the child's playground. It doesn't look out of place – it's become innocent hiding within the hopscotch – just as cancer is invisible and silent.
Lulu hasn't seen it yet, nor Anna who is stood out of view.
We don't want them to see it;
we want them to just play.
A retouched photo of my daughters tracing shadows.

We have a date.

SURGERY — (13th Feb).

— Anna's 5th Birthday

An appointment was made for **13th February.**

13th February was my daughter's 5th Birthday.

Despite my reeling inside at this unnatural reality, there was no option to avoid the inevitable.

Delaying surgery was not wise, I knew that.

Such is the power of love – it was not the surgery, the lumpectomy that I dreaded; it was not being with my daughter on her 5th birthday.

I have to thank Edvard Munch for this one! Recreating the famous painting to express my feelings of total desperation.
I am separated from my family in my own sad bubble of fate whilst my daughter celebrates her 5th Birthday.
In hindsight, Ian should have been in my bubble
as he also missed her birthday.
Mixed media – acrylics, pastels and photographic.

Umbilical Talk

I'll get through this — I won't tell Mum & Dad.
I'll tell them later when it's over.

Why give them the worry when they had enough of their own health issues going on? But somehow it just didn't feel right.

After much thought and deliberation, we decided that they would want to know. So, I set off on the two-and-a-half-hour journey to see them, to tell them. I called them when I was just five minutes away and announced my close proximity so that they wouldn't be too shocked to find me suddenly on the doorstep!

It was Mum who answered the phone and she sounded so pleased to hear my voice. When I arrived, we just sat around the kitchen table, Mum, Dad and me, no kettle boiling for tea and no small talk.

And I just said it straight out.

The weirdest thing was that they didn't seem shocked. They held themselves strong and we joked about me copying Mum (who had just closed the door on her own episode of breast cancer).

Mum said she felt that something wasn't right — she had said to Dad that I hadn't looked well for some time.

My brother, Tony, arrived to complete the family circle and we had one of the most lovely evenings together. We cooked a fabulous meal, had some wine and just enjoyed a rare occasion when just the four of us were together again under this roof, like so many times years before.

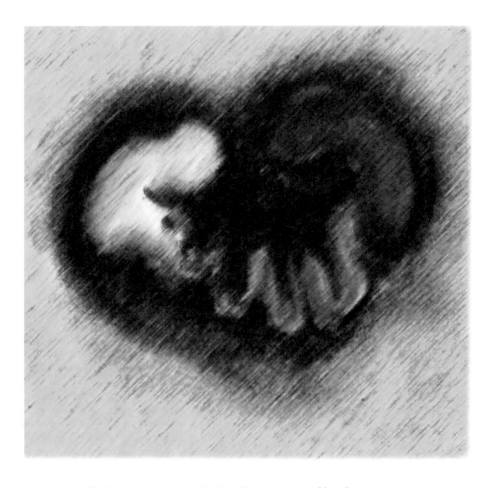

The heart represents the love between myself and my parents.
It's also like the womb containing me, keeping me safe.
I use the umbilical cord to show the bond between us.
As I'm drawing, the umbilical cord becomes also the nostalgic old style curly phone
cable. The phone plays a huge part in my link to my parents because of the physical
distance between us.
Oil pastels, and computer effects.

Lucky Me.

The wheels were set in motion for the girls to go to Nana and Grandad in Surrey, where my sister-in-law made plans to take them out for days with their cousins.

Meanwhile, I had time to get my head around things for my day ahead which seemed so much less daunting now that the girls were excited about their week.

They told me after the op that they couldn't believe I'd found this lump. In fact, what I had felt was granular breast tissue and a few innocent cysts, but it was what lurked deeper that posed the biggest threat.

I used to look at women going about their daily rituals of shopping, collecting kids from school, and I wanted to say to them, "Go and get checked out – in case you've got this too."

So from that moment, I took a different stance and acknowledged just how lucky I was to have found this, to be dealing with it and with time on my side.

Instead of viewing myself as the victim, I wanted this image to show me as the lucky
one. I am informed. I am in a position to be dealing with my situation.
It's everyone around me that I fear for – the question marks that lurk above them.
Ink sketch with computer effects.

All change

The follow up consultation after surgery was a really low point.

The pathology test from the lumpectomy had revealed a very small area of aggressive cancer, only 5mm in diameter. And the cancer had also spread beyond the margins of the area that had been removed in surgery.

This was such a shock; the forecast seemed to have taken a complete turnabout and the path ahead now looked so different from the one I was already focussed on.

Now I was facing a course of chemotherapy and a mastectomy.

There would be no short cuts and no running away.

We just sat like stone, and listened, my husband and I, and I felt as though I was floating way above and looking down on this unfortunate scene as if it were happening to someone else entirely.

And when we got home, we cried.

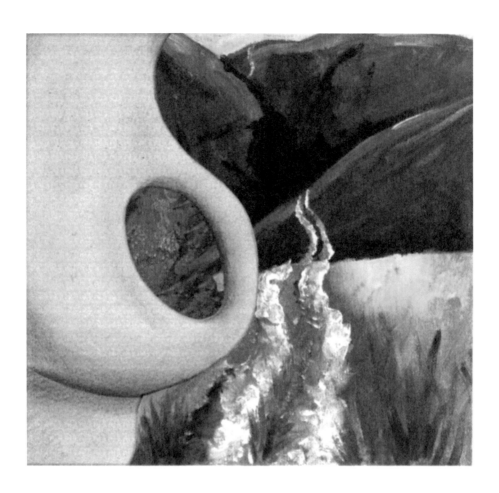

The view into the distance is looking gloomy with its hills and valleys
– the ups and downs ahead of me.
I used the hole through the breast to accentuate the idea that everything changed after
my surgery. The red spot marks the aggressive cancer which has now become a
significant part of my view ahead.
Body created from a pencil sketch. View into distance in acrylics.

((Expanding the circle))

We started to expand our circle of those-in-the-know, deciding it was now inevitable that people would realise. Since this journey was going to span at least the next 15 months instead of the short haul we had first thought, we would quite possibly need support from people around us.

Telling family and friends about the new forecast was not an easy conversation.

Somehow the words came like an echo of the consultant's words – trying to sound informed and in control, trying to swallow the wobbly voice to somehow protect everyone from the reality.

But people have big hearts and people are strong and we realised that we were strong too.

The circle (heart) dilates as we include more people in our world. Their hands reach out toward us with offers of support and friendship.
Ink marbling, pen, computer.

Chemo conception.

Getting my head around having chemo was so hard and I'm not quite sure why.

Another dreaded 'c' word.

I think it's because it's one of those words that is so riddled with pre-conceived images that you fail to see it for what it is:

A treatment, by means of chemicals to destroy cancerous tissue.

It's also one of those words that somehow applies to others, but never yourself.

The next few weeks were turbulent, emotionally.

Trying to press on with our day-to-day existence but with this big black cloud hanging – overshadowing the normality of everything.

I used a photo that Ian had taken, as a backdrop to show how I was feeling. Normal life continued way below me but I felt isolated and traumatised in this new surreal place that I found myself floating in. The sun is shining on me, it's bright and there's nowhere to hide.
I know that I must have chemo

Pre-chemo

Before the chemotherapy treatments could start, there were a number of health issues to satisfy – a CT body scan, a heart scan and a blood pool scan – all to ensure that I was fit enough to withstand the battering of the strong chemo drugs.

I also had a pre-chemo talk with my support nurse to be informed of the possible side-effects of the chemo.

In my naivety, I had anticipated that it would be a heart-to-heart – an emotional buffering – but instead it was an honest, detailed rendition of all the possible side effects of chemo treatment.

The single most terrifying aspect of the chemotherapy was the simple fact that there were no certainties.

Sometimes the thought of something is worse than the reality, I certainly found that I felt better (emotionally) once I'd passed that start line.

And it's important to remember that there is a legal obligation to inform patients about all the possible side effects of treatment, even though most people only experience a few symptoms in reality.

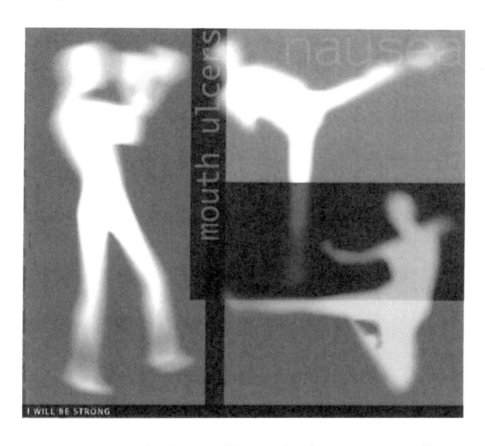

This image I created in the style of X-rays to show how strong I felt, and how determined I was to fight for my health.
Sketches distorted on computer.

Tears of laughter!

How do you tell your children that you'll possibly - no probably lose your hair?

It never seemed to be the right moment to explain this one, but the right moment did come.

I waited until they were busy doing some cutting and sticking so that it would seem more casual. I told them that not all of the 'hurty' was gone and so the doctors were going to give me some strong medicine to get rid of the 'hurty' that was still there. And I explained that the medicine wasn't clever enough to just find the bad bits, it sometimes hurt the good bits too.

I spoke of a sore mouth, and weak discoloured finger nails, and then I just said the words:

"Mummy's hair may fall out."

I don't think in a million years I could have predicted the reaction from my five year old.

She looked at her sister and with eyebrows raised and a huge grin she said: "Mummy's going to be bald!"

Then she laughed; they both laughed; we all laughed.

How unpredictable children are.
What was a huge revelation in my world, was actually funny in their world!
The choice of collage for this image was used quite simply because I had chosen a time
when they were busy with cutting and sticking to deliver my forecast of baldness.
Collage created with the girls.

Comedy :)

*Choosing a wig was actually fun!
It became one of the comedy moments
in these pre-treatment weeks.*

The first wig I tried on was promising once carefully arranged around my face (which would have benefitted now from some make-up). But from there on, they went downhill fast as I dared to explore new exciting identities; a new me for the journey ahead.

By the time I'd tried on about six or so wigs, my own hair was practically moulded flat onto my head, and as the stylist removed the wig, my husband and I cried out at the same time:

No! Put it back on!!

A couple were shortlisted, and after eliminating the culprits that turned me into the lead singer of Sweet, we finally had my new hairstyle.

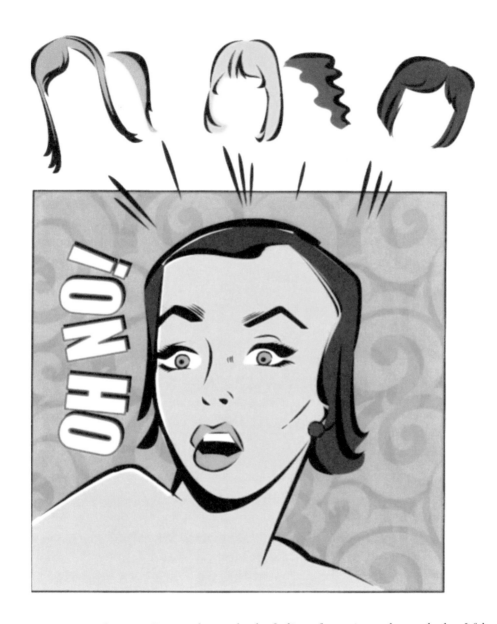

This pop art style image I created to evoke the feeling of surprise and comedy that I felt when it was my own hair that looked so desperate, and not the wigs that I tried on! Drawn on computer in illustrator.

Into the Abyss ⟶

The meeting with the support nurse to advise on the possible side effects of the chemotherapy was, as I've said, quite daunting.

So many side effects

I didn't envy the support nurse with this task of informing and educating patients.

In hindsight, I wonder if it's better to be informed or to not know anything?

I mean, would someone refuse chemo because their nails might discolour, or because they might get a sore mouth?

Surely anything is tolerable in exchange for your life.

The most terrifying aspect of chemo was the simple fact that there were no certainties; no clear forecast of how I would react to the drugs or how effective the treatments would be in the long term.

I felt as though I was stepping into the abyss with a blindfold on.

Sinking under water, deep below life and light. The heavy weight of the horseshoe as a symbol of lucky/unlucky depending on how it falls.
The 'C' shape of the horseshoe – another C for cancer.

Silly wigs!

The girls didn't like the idea of me wearing a wig – they said I'd look silly.

I smile inside to think what they must have imagined with their knowledge of wigs being restricted to clowns and witches in their dressing-up box!

So I sat them in front of the Postiche website and let them trawl through all manner of wigs to see how good they in fact were.

When I went back 20 minutes later, I found them chatting busily as they compiled lists of their favourite wigs.

It gave me a lump in my throat to see them so totally involved, seeming to accept the idea and even finding it fun.

Faces on eggs – a joint effort between my girls and me.
Using eggs came about by chance but made us laugh to see them come to life with
drawn faces.

Hello!
It's still ME in here!

It may sound odd, (ungrateful even), but when I was facing up to this trauma, it didn't help me to talk about it all the time. It sometimes felt as if people didn't know what else to talk about with me.

I just wanted everyone to treat me like normal and for conversations to centre on something, anything other than my illness.

I was still the same person inside, needing stimulation, needing to laugh.

And yet I knew that people were being caring and showing this in the only way that felt appropriate.

This shows the 'me' inside me.
Trapped, caught between the stream of serious conversations
and the yearning for normality and humour.
Collage and computer.

The First Chemo.

If I said I wasn't nervous about my first chemo treatment, I would be lying.

It felt insurmountable to me and almost as if it was someone else going through the motions instead of me.

I'd been introduced to the chemo suite the week before so I had been well prepared. The atmosphere within the suite couldn't have been more different from what I'd expected. Big comfortable chairs each housed a smiling, sleeping or reading patient, drinking tea or eating a sandwich. Nurses that quietly went about their work, gently caring for their allocated patients, to an incessant musical backdrop of little beeps as the last chemo dripped down into the patient.

Once the procedure was under way, I felt much calmer and with my husband by my side, the three hours passed smoothly. I felt jaded, emotionally tired more than anything. As time went on, I felt a little shivery and spaced out; it's a hard feeling to explain, but I felt OK and for that I was very grateful.

There was a shocking amount of medication to take during the four days that followed; all manner of meds to counteract the possible side effects.

On the fifth day, it was a huge relief to not be clock-watching for tablets. And I felt fine.

fear   hope   love   willpower   anger

I wanted to express how daunting that very first step was, and how once the journey
had started, other emotions took over.
Interestingly, I felt very little anger.

Acrylics and computer effects.

Watercress and Potato Soup

Ingredients:

A whole portion of love
209-mile round trip by car
food shopping on route
approx. 6 hours

I am embarrassed to admit it but when my sister-in-law decided to drive down from Cheshire to cook me up some watercress and potato soup, it had the most profound effect on me. Instead of being touched by such a kind gesture, I reacted very badly.

Her surprise visit stunned me; I didn't really know what to say apart from how crazy she was to have gone to such lengths.

But later when she was home again, having prepared and stacked tubs of soup into my freezer, I felt agitated and angry.

What she had done for me —
as a gesture of care and love
— had made me feel useless,
— it had magnified my vision
of myself as someone with an illness.

I sent the nastiest text message explaining how I felt.

We laugh about it today and she admits in hindsight that it wasn't the right thing to have done, but sometimes when you care about someone, you want to put your love into a positive gesture.

Looking back, I can see how sensitive and emotional I was, and I realised then just how hard it is to be on the other side of the fence, watching someone you care for, going through such uncertain times.

Just a bowl of soup.
Made with love and the very best intentions.
And yet it released such a huge wave of emotion.
Created on computer.

Re-location.

We'd made plans to rent a house in the next village, to escape the mayhem and dust of our cottage which was still mid- building project as I got my diagnosis. Building materials and dust do not mix well with chemotherapy!

The house and garden was big and, more importantly, it was well-placed for the girls to still qualify for the school bus. We were determined to keep their world steady and as consistent as possible.

I had an overwhelming feeling that I wanted this summer to be lodged in their minds as - The summer in the White house with the swings - and not the summer when Mummy was ill.

Papers were signed and we collected the key and started the big move on the morning after my first chemo treatment.

With help from family, (and minimal input from me as I curled up on the sofa and watched), we did it – first chemo and moved house within 24 hours!

Looking through a keyhole – our secret new home for the summer – and the novelty of
a big garden for the girls to play in.
Watercolour, pencils and charcoal.

Carry on Living!

Well before my diagnosis, we'd booked a cottage on the Gower peninsula in south Wales for Easter, to take my parents and meet up with my brother and family.

It was about a week after my first chemo treatment and I felt ok, so it seemed the only logical thing was to carry on as planned.

It was wonderful to see the sea and feel the wind through my hair (which I still had), but best of all was watching the children bursting with sheer excitement when they discovered the indoor pool!

Although I couldn't go in the pool, for risk of an infection, it was one of the most special holidays ever.

It took no orchestration, just a close-knit family enjoying time together in a lovely environment.

Easter card made by Anna.
A really special Easter, despite my illness, made special by enjoying time with family
and watching the children play with their cousins.

PLUMMET.

Day 9. Easter Sunday. Not feeling good.

My mouth felt so sore and ulcerated - and nothing quite tasted as I expected.

It reminded me of the metallic taste you get during pregnancy. I felt really tearful. I had no energy and I couldn't make the beach walk with the others.

Two days later and my energy was back!

I felt great.

We headed to the beach for more digging, paddling and collecting shells.

I'm sure it was the wind on that beach that speeded the demise of my hair less than a week later!

Photo taken on holiday in Wales.
A 'Get Well Soon' card
from me to me.
How quickly moods can change from one day to the next
under chemo.

Bald and Bold.

In hindsight, I should have guessed because my scalp felt tingly and very tender to touch.

I was at home in the bathroom with my daughter, and as I ran my fingers through my hair, a great handful of hair came away entwined in my fingers.

"It's coming out now, Mummy, isn't it?" she said.

Her little sister appeared around the door looking intrigued, followed by my husband, who gauging the landmark situation announced casually that he was so pleased because it meant that the medicine was working well.

And that was that.

Handful upon handful of hair came away, and when I decided that the patchy look wasn't for me, I am wet-shaved my head.

A new very different-looking Mummy appeared, and after a little apprehension, a few giggles and some head stroking, the girls accepted this new version of me.

Photo taken in my friend Clare's hair salon (after chemo).
Incidentally it's not my hair, but I couldn't resist taking this photo, lured by the way it
sat across the X of the floor tiles.

A Beacon.

It's funny how you change your thoughts along the way.

I had my mind firmly set on wearing a wig. I had chosen a wig and it looked pretty good; a continuation of me, only much better groomed, thicker, tidier, as if I'd just left the hair salon.

And that, was the problem.

When it came to wearing it, it just didn't feel right.

I suddenly realised that I would be in effect 'hiding away', hiding the real me. I only wore my wig once and couldn't wait to tear it off.

From then on, I wore a bandana, a cap or a scarf – grateful for the power it had as a beacon to those all around me – speaking on my behalf so that I didn't have to.

Painting by Lulu. Mummy wearing her favourite bandana.

Therapy

My lovely mum came with me for my second treatment.

Ian dropped us off about 20 minutes early and we seized the opportunity to squeeze in a bit of retail-therapy before the chemo-therapy.

A handbag and scarf later, we scurried to the chemo suite and to check in.

It was a nice diversion, and made the day feel more normal – after all, Shopping is what Mum and I did best!

It was wonderful to have Mum beside me, and a huge comfort for her to see first-hand the treatment and the environment where I was to spend so many hours.

Other than her amazement at the sheer volume of drugs that were administered, she was comforted by the warmth of the chemo suite environment and the tenderness that the nurses showed to their patients.

I wanted to show the togetherness of Mum and me, sharing the joy of something as simple as a bit of retail therapy.
Created on computer from sketches.

A flood of emotions.

My second chemo hit me differently, harder.

It's difficult to translate the feeling into words but I just felt much more emotional.

On day 7 after my treatment, I hit rock bottom and I felt really tearful.

No, let's be honest, I felt angry for the first time. I felt really angry with the world.

I wallowed in my mood and I cried, and by the following day, I was back up on top again.

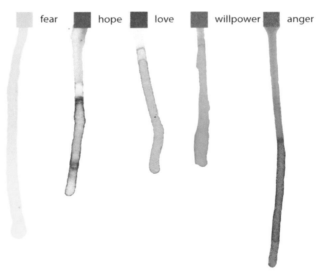

Using colour to show the mix of emotions.

CONFLICT

Generally speaking, I don't do things by halves, so it was no surprise that having had my initial surgery on my youngest daughter's 5th Birthday, that my next chemo fell on my older daughter's 8th Birthday.

In fact, it seemed that every treatment or check-up clashed with a school event, a sports day or a special assembly.

For me it was these sacrifices that made the commitment to this illness so heavy and so utterly consuming.

On one hand, I had to accept that nothing else was as important as my treatment, and yet, I resented missing these special landmark events in my daughters' lives.

Text and balloons added to mark the demands and burden of the illness versus the colour and joy of family life.
Photo taken of sunset over our village.

Rock Solid

You learn a lot about people throughout this process. It never ceased to amaze me how many people have either been through this illness or know someone who has. If ever I doubted human nature, this journey restored my faith.

It was the understated 'rock solid' love and support that I felt from family and friends that kept me buoyant.

One of the hardest things was making sure we had plans in place for the girls if we got delayed at hospital (which was not uncommon), but we had good friends who we relied on time and time again.

I met people who said they felt for me going through this with two young children, but I never saw it like that. In my world, these two loving daughters made me strong; comforted me when I felt sad and gave me the determination to cherish the simple and beautiful things in life.

And Ian, my husband, was relentless in his care and optimism. I knew that I had the best person in the world to get me through this (still smiling, still laughing).

One evening not long after I became bald, we were sat in the kitchen and it was raining heavily outside. And he just looked across at me and told me that I looked beautiful.

He made me feel beautiful.

Rock solid love. I wanted to freeze that moment like a statue.
Photo taken in Summer 2012 sat in the garden
- computer effect to look like rock.

Mirror, mirror on the wall

I took my mum a cup of tea in bed one morning when she was staying (to keep me company).

As I walked past the mirror in her room, I caught sight of myself and jumped out of my skin with surprise, spilling her tea.

I had completely forgotten that I was bald!

(The funny thing was, it wasn't as if it was even the morning after I'd lost my hair!)

We laughed so much about that.

Making use of the egg again.
I saw nothing else in that mirror except
a big round bald head!

3rd Chemo

My daughter's 8th Birthday (and my 3rd chemo treatment).

It was by far my worst session.

They had difficulty getting the canula into my puny veins and it took three nurses four attempts before it was safely inserted. My positivity and strength escaped me completely after two attempts which were painful, and I felt as if I was screaming inside.

I wanted to run away – to just get up and leave the chemo suite.

A curtain was drawn around me to give me some privacy (and I suspect also to screen me off from the other patients).

Ian calmed me and the male nurse who arrived from the children's ward performed the task swiftly and painlessly.

At that moment, I just wanted to run away.
Sketch on computer.

Tablet time

For the four days after a treatment, there were plenty of tablets to take.

It was quite a schedule – and I always seemed to be playing catch-up.

The tablets were to prevent nausea, vomiting, acid reflux and some steroids (to do what steroids do). And they worked wonders – I was never sick and only very occasionally did I feel a bit nauseous.

Bingo!

On day 5, the tablets stopped and it was a huge relief to not be clock watching.

Time was a blur – just an ongoing schedule of tablets
to help me feel as OK as possible. I tried to think of the tablets
like little sweets.
Created on computer.

Food frenzy

The metallic taste in my mouth reminded me of pregnancy. On one hand, food was like an obsession, and yet I was nearly always disappointed with how things tasted. I couldn't drink tea at all which was quite a shock since beforehand I was a complete tea lady.

After a few days with headaches, it suddenly dawned on me that I might be suffering from caffeine withdrawal!

So I gave white coffee a try, which was surprisingly nice and far more palatable than tea.

I found that strong, spicy flavours were much more satisfying (even though the flavour was different to that lodged in my memory).

Sometimes when I stared into the fridge for an inkling of an idea of what to eat, I felt like an alien taste-testing food for the first time!

As I peered into the fridge for inspiration, I really felt like an alien tasting things for the first time.
Pastels and computer effects.

Never the right time

When cancer arrives, it's never the right time; there never is a right time.

I had been working on a project for several years, to encourage creativity and imaginative thinking in children. I was at a critical stage, with some very positive feedback from retailers and I was determined to carry on as normal, but I had no idea what impact the chemo drugs would have on me.

I suppose I knew that it was inevitable that the project would be relegated to a lower division for the duration of my treatment.

And this got me thinking about 'time'.

I've heard people say that they're too busy to be ill
(as if it's optional).
But when you are ill, you view your life in a different way

It separates the things that are important from those that are not important at all. And the simple things in life suddenly become precious whilst rushing around and meeting deadlines seemed so utterly futile.

The things in life that felt precious and important – like my daughters walking over the fields, laughing together or pulling up some enormous rhubarb in the garden, or simply the way that the light catches the edge of a leaf.
Things that used to be important have now faded.
Original photos/graphics and drawings.

Family

How much harder this journey would have been without my family around me.

My husband knew when to make me laugh and when I needed to cry. He steered me along optimistically and pulled me back in line if I drifted into the depths of the forest.

He always offered a reasoned and logical forecast to light the shadows of my thoughts.

My daughters were old enough, even at five and eight, to be a rock to me; they were my friends and my focus throughout.

They took responsibility when needed, they were my legs when I lacked energy, they stroked me and showed me love along the way, and they adapted to all these changes without treating me any differently.

I have become the infant, curled up like a foetus in the womb.
Ian leads the way through the dark forest and it is my girls that carry me.
We are all naked, in our purest, truest form like animals.
Painted in acrylics and computer effects added.

A Lost day.

Day 6 of my third chemo cycle was a lost day; a day that needed to be forgotten. It's hard to explain how a bad day under chemo feels.

It's not like a bad day not under chemo.

It's as if someone had torn me from within myself, and all that was left was an empty shell.

I went through the motions of eating and sleeping but somehow, I felt trapped in a fog and try as I did, I just couldn't connect or engage with anything at all.

Day 7 arrived and bingo!

I couldn't wait to have a shower and get going with the day!

Floating outside myself.
An emptiness. A blur.
Cut out paper and computer.

In the Club

It was about this time, for the first time, that I almost wished I could talk to someone else going through this. I had such great support from family and friends but I couldn't help thinking that they couldn't really know how I felt because they hadn't experienced this journey first-hand.

I had been so determined to not get involved in 'comparison' chats with other sufferers.

I knew from my oncologist that two people with the same diagnosis at the same age could react in totally different ways so I struggled to see the benefit of sharing stories.

In the end, I decided to resist the urge to speak to others 'in the club'.

I only had myself to gauge and I felt that I would cope better without benchmarking against anyone else.

I am me. I shall not compare.

I only wore my wig once
and my nails were so you suck out it
Did you didn't have that at all didn't last long.
off you buy a wig?
My mouth was so sore much weight!
I'm so tired all the time my bum the street
and I actually fell over in the nothing tasted right

...were yours?

Did you didn't have that at all didn't last long.
or did you shave it off?

I wanted this image to convey the emotional turmoil that I felt could be caused by comparing details with other people.
Ink marbling background, text overlaid.

Look good = feel better.

I can honestly say that wherever possible this journey was made as pleasant as it could be.

Free parking was amongst the perks! The other was a complimentary beauty session at the hospital, led by a group of beauticians.

Ordinarily, I would never have gone for this, but with the prospect of losing my eyelashes and eyebrows and not having a clue how I would make myself look half decent, I booked in for it.

It was a group session, with light-hearted banter from an unlikely group of women who all shared one common denominator.

We all wanted to feel better by looking good (or as good as possible)!

Not only did we learn how to simulate eyelashes and eyebrows with an eyeliner pencil, we also learnt how to create a healthy glow, and we all left clutching a beauty bag full of cosmetics.

The simplicity and joy of a session of beauty therapy, experimenting with colours and tone just like a child with a colouring book.

The Palm Reading

Funny how your mind wanders.

Either I had more time to muse over things or perhaps suddenly everything seemed more precious.

I started to think about things from years ago. I think the brain is so incredible in its ability to bring thoughts to the forefront; thoughts that were seemingly inconsequential.

So, why on that particular sunny afternoon did my brain churn out a memory from 18 years earlier?

I was on a works party and met a palm reader who offered to tell me my fortune. She studied me for simply ages and I remember being shocked when finally she relayed a forecast of drugs that would feature heavily in my future.

I can't say I've thought about it much from then until now – when it has amassed an uncanny significance.

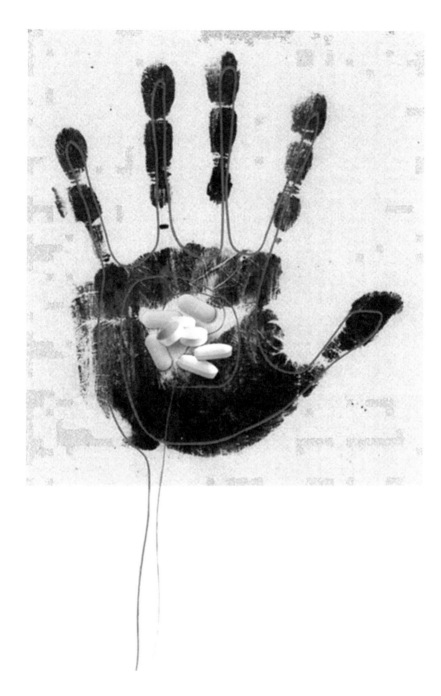

My hand printed in black ink – I had perceived my drug dependency as a negative addiction, but in fact the chemo drugs saved me.

Single or Double Scoop?

I was thinking ahead to the surgery, the mastectomy that I would have after the six months of chemo. It will be like the intermission before the next chemo, but without the ice cream.

A mastectomy. Single or double scoop? I decided in the end to have a double mastectomy, although I had to fight hard for them to agree to it. Apparently, it's not ethical to remove a healthy breast and there wasn't anything wrong with my right breast.

But I just didn't feel that I wanted to spend every day wondering if all was still well.

My entire life had been questioned, and in real terms losing my breasts (although I liked them plenty) was not important by comparison with time here with my daughters, my family and friends.

Of course it was daunting, but I got used to the idea over a long period of time, and in the end I just saw it for what it was — logical, sensible and necessary.

I shudder when I think that some women apparently refuse to have a mastectomy; I wish I could have spoken to them.

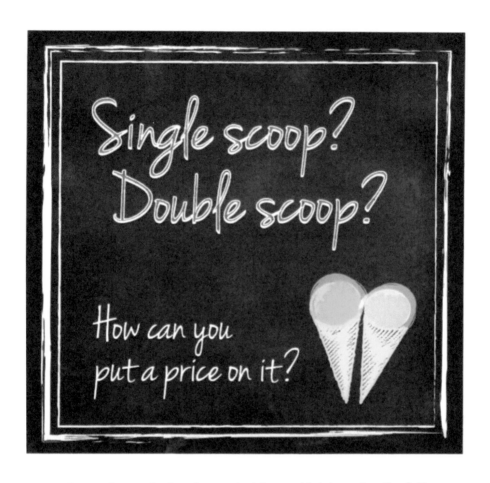

I wanted to emphasise the fact that my decision couldn't be rationalised. No matter what the medics said about ethics, I needed to be rid of both my breasts to feel complete and to move on with my life.

escape

I've always been pretty good at sleeping, apart from when the girls were very young. The experts were quite surprised that I was getting good sleep despite the steroids in the treatment. I am quite sure that sleep, for me, is my escape route.

And when I wasn't asleep,
I read books.
Lots of books.

Not only did they make time pass more quickly when I was having a treatment, but they transported me to another place where I escaped the reality of the here and now.

This image shows how I used reading as a way of lifting myself up out of the doom and gloom. Although cancer was always somewhere in my mind (the tilted 'c' in ESCAPE), books, stories and characters took me away to another place.
My temporary escape.
Mixed media; acrylics, collage and computer graphics.

Reflecting on the Past.

I became very nostalgic about old friends and good times past.

I don't think it was solely the result of my current situation; I think it's also what happens when you get to be mid-forty.

I spent time going through old photos and videos of the girls when they were babies, toddlers.

I also traced some friends from university and school and enjoyed exchanges on email, seeing what people's lives had dealt them.

I didn't always share my news, my illness.
Sometimes it just pleased me more not to mention it.

The dolls represent snapshots of my life at different times from birth; age 3 years; age 12 years; age 28 years; and age 48 years. The nostalgia I felt brought back poignant and vivid memories of my life and my friendships.
Russian dolls painted and photographed.

Weedy veins.

Some days the veins in my right forearm were so ropey that you could almost play them like a guitar (accompanied by a nice drum beat on my bald head!).

My oncologist struck off my last chemo treatment of the first drug cycle because my veins were really suffering, becoming ropey and withdrawn.

Funny how veins can disappear as if they're hiding!

He also recommended me for a Portacath to be fitted in my chest so that I could receive my treatment without the struggle of the 'find-a-vein' game!

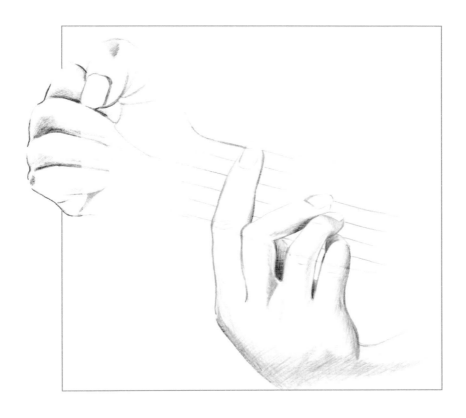

My veins became ropey and as they withdrew,
they left tracks in my arm – like guitar strings.
The fist clenched in the way that you clench and release it to pump up the veins
before a treatment.
Pencil drawing.

A New Drug called Taxol.

My next chemo treatment was Taxol and I was to have it weekly as a weaker strain than the hard-hitting 3 weekly cycle. I later discovered that this drug came from the yew tree; funny then that we have a huge yew tree in the middle of the garden.

As with all change and uncertainty comes apprehension.

The insertion of the canula through the Portacath went quite smoothly, albeit slightly sore. I could imagine my veins sigh with the sheer relief.

This session was by far the longest. I had optimistically and perhaps somewhat naively planned in my head to get to my daughter's school sports day that afternoon. Ian went instead and after a marathon seven hours, I was finally disconnected.

The clock ticking as I had my first Taxol chemo treatment.
The treatment which was considerably longer than I had realised – overshadowing all hope of getting to my daughter's sports day.
Photo montage.

Proverbial BIN !

One thing that was good about weekly treatments was that I got to tick them off more quickly. My sister-in-law introduced me to the idea – she used this technique when she was having contractions during labour.

Every time she finished a contraction, she would mentally screw it up and throw it in the f***ing bin.

I found this mental strategy worked well – and every time I finished a treatment, I would text her to announce another one in the proverbial bin!

After each treatment, I could mentally screw it up
and throw it away.

Freewheeling

Another Taxol cycle came and went, and another Herceptin.

The treatments became shorter and smoother, and other than a little fatigue afterwards, I was lucky enough to suffer no major side effects.

I felt as though I was freewheeling now having reached a stage of familiarity with the procedure, the staff and the environment.

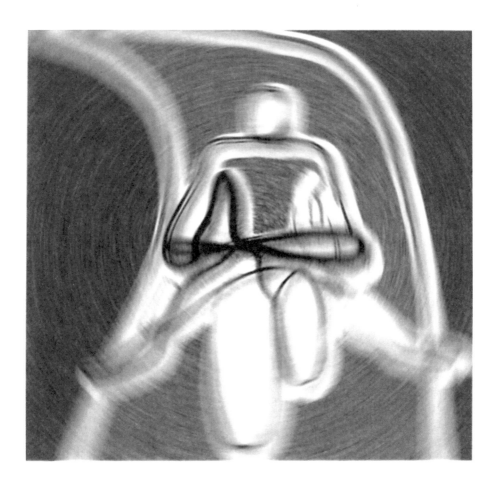

This image shows how the journey became familiar as time went on. There was a new-found freedom in the familiarity, as if I was over the hilltop and could see the finish line and I was freewheeling towards it.
Drawn in Illustrator on computer.

Weight

I was shocked to find that in less
than three months,
I had piled on 6lb!

I had been warned about this and realised that it was the steroids that made me feel so hungry. I decided to change my diet and to start to do some exercise.

I had done Pilates since the birth of my first daughter so I was fairly confident that I could do it from home. I couldn't face up to going to my usual class and losing my head scarf in the roll-down. Silly really because everyone would have been great to me but sometimes you just can't face up to some things.

So I did Pilates from home. I was shattered even after a very short session but I felt heaps better for having done it, mentally and physically.

*The figure represents 'the child's pose' in Pilates but with my arms beside me,
protecting me. Floating on top of the clouds in the warm sunlight, with the positive
feeling I got from doing Pilates.*
Clay sculpture montaged with photo taken by Ian.

Apricots!

I tried to eat foods rich in iron to help to restore a healthy blood count. Meal times took red meat as centre stage and snacks took the shape of fresh fruit and lots of dried apricots.

In fact, far too many dried apricots!

I had to re-think this diet once I realised that I was incapable of taking more than two steps without passing wind!

SEVERE WEATHER WARNING

* TORNADO* WARNING

* **Tornado:** A violently rotating column of air, with circulation reaching the ground. It nearly always starts as a funnel cloud and may be accompanied by a loud roaring noise.

The weather warning reporting on the severe reaction
I had to the dried apricots!

Head wear.

Hats, scarves and bandanas – I got so bored of wearing them all.

It's a funny thing but I genuinely didn't feel that concerned about losing my hair. I knew it would happen, I prepared myself and I found the experience sort of liberating.

I only wore the wig once. When I was at home, I rarely wore anything on my head but as soon as I stepped outside into the big world of prying eyes, I always wore something on my head. It became a sort of pressure, a compulsory action.

I sat watching my daughters in their swim classes whilst craving to tear the hat off my head, and I chatted in the playground from beneath the peak of my hat.

Carrying the 'psychological' weight of all this headwear. Despite enjoying freedom from headwear in the privacy of my home, I just couldn't bring myself to go bald in public because of the fear of everyone's eyes on me.
Image created on computer.

Sinking.

I lay on my bed on the evening of my third Taxol treatment, listening to my girls singing and playing in the bath. Their voices distorted by the sounds of splashing water and yet also echoey.

I felt as though I was sinking under water, submerged in my feelings of remoteness and I just lay there reflecting on how I came to be here.

I felt remote from reality, submerged in my gloom and yet gradually my mood lifted, as if the familiarity of the girls' banter was pulling me out of a bad dream.

By the following morning, I was back on top again.

I felt distant and remote as I lay listening to my girls playing in the bath.
And gradually their banter and giggling brought me back to the surface.

No Seat Cred!

It's amazing how desperate you get!

I was settling into my chair waiting for my treatment to start. I did my usual panoramic scan of the chemo suite trying to see who was assigned to do my treatment. On seeing the male nurse who had saved the day on my third treatment, I smiled and felt assured that he was the one for today.

Then out of the blue, a female nurse, unknown to me, introduced herself and started assembling the usual paraphernalia on top of the trolley. As panic started to set in, I decided to take action. Shifting from one buttock to the other I sat tall and on catching his eye I mouthed as clearly as possible 'I want you'.

He smiled a nervous smile and gave a little shrug. So again, I mouthed 'I want you'. An awkward silent laugh came back from him and he subtly pointed at the female nurse and mouthed 'she is good.' So I was forced to surrender to her – and he was right, she was good.

I couldn't help but see the funny side of this later that night. Not helped by the fact that I looked particularly hideous on that occasion; having decided to wear 'comfy' tracky bottoms that kept riding up my shins when I sat down. And the good-looking male nurse who was going about his duties, with all his expertise and skill, to be accosted and silently summoned by the words 'I want you' from this most hideous vision!

I used this free hand-drawn style to show the humour that I felt later that evening when the treatment was finished!

4th Taxol.

My mother-in-law came with me for my fourth Taxol treatment. Having been a theatre nurse, she found the experience really interesting and was hugely impressed with this professional and upbeat environment.

Unfortunately, I developed very sore nostrils after this treatment and I had a screaming cold unlike any I had ever had before.

It took the form of sudden and unexpected gushes of fluid from the nostrils, typically when I was mid conversation with someone!

I actually contemplated attaching a small cup to the end of my nose.

Instead, a tube of antiseptic nasal cream seemed to do the trick and the symptoms gradually subsided.

All focus on my nose and nostrils – when my nose streamed, it gushed and was out of control. Also the idea of tears as it was making me feel really low.
Hand drawn linework with computer effects.

Schizophrenic Climate

It was a really strange summer for weather.

A totally schizophrenic climate making it virtually impossible to plan anything. Even within half an hour, sunshine would become heavy rain and the sky seemed to be permanently playing out an animation.

I couldn't help feeling that these mood swings in nature reflected how I was feeling inside.

I was fighting to stay positive but couldn't help the black clouds and tears that overcame me from time to time.

I didn't have very many of these dark days and the few that I did have, came and went leaving me feeling free again.

Painting by Lulu.
I had my daughter's picture up on the wall in my office. It always spoke to me – it's
clouds, some angry and some hopeful, tears of joy and tears of pain.
The wet summer of 2012 with its clouds crying.
The scan-like shadows of threatening clouds lurking behind colourful clouds.
The idea of veins and blood.
And of course the chemo drugs dripping slowly down through the tube to do their work.

Partnership

I've heard people say that getting through this can make or break a relationship. I can see how it could stretch you to the limit, although for us it was a process we just had to get through, and together we took one step at a time.

For the vast majority of the time, I felt focussed and life ran its course as normal, but occasionally I crumbled, tipped over the edge by something trivial or small. On these occasions, Ian would listen, mop up my desperation and mould it back into something positive.

He seemed to connect with my moods and was able to steer me into better times.

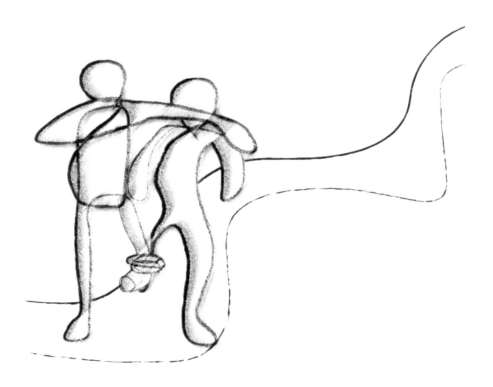

The partnership that I had with my husband was like a three-legged race, we learnt that we needed to be in sync with each other and take it step by step to get around the burden of our legs being tied, or in our case the challenges of the chemo journey.

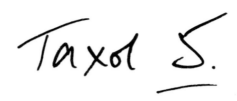

Taxol 5.

Treatment 5 came and went OK.

We managed to secure an appointment with my oncologist. A very fitting day to have had such an enlightening meeting with my professor, coinciding with our daughters watching the Olympic torch passing their school on its onward journey.

We made the decision to opt for a full 12 months of Herceptin treatment, based on the assurance that my heart was in good enough shape to withstand it.

It's easier to keep running whilst you're on the road than to stop and face the possibility of starting this journey again.

Just like the Olympic torch needed to keep going, so did I.
My heart like a balloon was celebrating its resilience
to this drug.

Getting things in Perspective

I always thought of questions to ask when I was half way home after an appointment, or I felt embarrassed to ask something that I thought sounded ridiculous.

On this occasion though, I decided to ask the question that lurked in my mind, and asked if there was still a chance of the cancer returning after a double mastectomy?

Not so silly a question after all, the answer came back to bite us. The chances of a recurrence are massively reduced but yes, there is a very small chance that residual breast tissue or cancer cells could recur on the chest wall.

I thought about this over the days ahead and then decided that it needed to be put into some sort of perspective. Bearing in mind that every patient is unique when it comes to cancer, it's hard to rationalise the risk of a recurrence. And what's the good of reading about probabilities on the Internet?

Did you know?

Coconuts kill about 150 people every year, falling from 80ft at an impact speed of 50mph. 24,000 people are killed each year by lightning strikes. More than 2,500 left-handed people are killed from using equipment meant for right-handed people, the power saw being the most deadly item.

I decided to get on with my life and not to dwell on statistics.

I felt angry towards all the statistics. I kicked them away so I could move on with my life.

Rollercoaster

At times when I let my spirits dip, I felt guilty and had to get a grip on myself and remind myself about the family and friends all rooting for me.

I felt as though I was a million miles away from the person I used to be.

It's hard to explain but I don't think I'll ever revert to being the person I used to be - before cancer.
Maybe that's a good thing.

Perhaps I will be a stronger and better person for the experience.

Photo of a paint palette. As I stared at this palette, the movement and the sweeps of colour seemed to echo my feelings.
I am small as I peer at this huge vision. I am looking at something that is powerful and threatening, and yet somehow it is also very beautiful.

CHEMO BRAIN

The school holidays were looming fast and we were trying to schedule the weeks ahead so that the girls had clubs and play days arranged to keep them entertained. Trying to co-ordinate with friends and family whilst avoiding treatment and blood test days was totally stressing me out.

I remembered how my mum had become frantic about hospital appointments and treatments when she went through breast cancer.

I felt brain-dead and struggled to keep my head around everything.

Apparently, it's called chemo brain!

In addition to this, it was time to make decisions about our own house, ordinarily a nice task; choosing a kitchen, an ensuite bathroom, not to mention new doors and a porch.

But for me, it was stressful and everything became blurred and demanding.

decide on kitchen units, what style? what colour?

up at the showroom...

...need to choose tiles...

...the house need to chan...

really need to decide on a porch...

Aaaaaarghhhhhhhhhhhhhhhh I just don't care about any of it

The chaos inside my head – as if everything was jumbled up and I couldn't string two thoughts together, let alone make decisions. I couldn't separate thoughts and deal with them individually – they just built up inside like a pressure.

Created on computer.

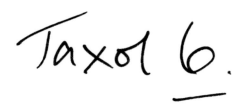

Taxol 6.

My sixth treatment day arrived, and so did a sickness bug in school.

Lulu spent the day vomiting and Ian played nurse, whilst trying to still attempt to get some work done.

And for the first time,
I faced up to my treatment
alone.

Apart from the usual chaos of finding a parking space, the treatment went well and I left hospital with a sense of pride and independence in having managed the day single-handedly.

Getting through the day on my own felt like walking through a long tunnel, and yet I emerged at the other end feeling stronger because I'd done it alone.
Image created on computer.

Endurance

I reached a state of mind where I felt trapped within myself, with no escape.

Ticking off treatments was good for a while, but then it seemed to become irrelevant and even the encouragement from people didn't really touch the surface of how I was feeling.

> I felt detached and distant.
> It wasn't the physical state I
> was in, it was the psychological
> state of my mind.

Thank goodness for my family and my daughters who kept me feeling special. Not only did they adapt to changes in their world; moving to another house, accepting their new bald mummy, but they stayed on track in their school lives and both brought home outstanding end-of-year reports!

It was as if they knew that this was the best tonic for me.

Just as I was losing enthusiasm for my own progress, I was able to focus on my girls'
progress at school – which lifted me again out of the gloom.
Hand drawn figure. Computer effects.

Bonds.

On my seventh Taxol treatment, I met a very special lady who had a profound effect on me. She had embraced her forecast of just 12 months' life expectancy, and yet she was still willing to undergo a gruelling schedule of treatments for six hours every day for four weeks on a clinical trial of a new drug.

She was resigned to her fate
but willing to give something back
that may help others in the future.

It never ceased to amaze me how selfless some people can be, whilst others live their lives in such stark contrast.

The bonds you make on this
journey may be short lived
but they are deep.

I will never forget my three-hour friendship with Barbara.

*Two simple brush strokes drawn on computer in grey and pink, to symbolise our paths
crossing. The heart shape that's formed between them – the deep bond between us.
(Also reminiscent of the breast cancer ribbon).*

Reaching a Plateau

There didn't seem to be a pattern to my symptoms like there had been on my first chemo drug. One minute I'd feel fine and the next I would be robbed of my energy and could barely hold my head up.

But all those bad bits passed and I reached a sort of plateau where I didn't really know how I felt anymore. I could see the goal in the distance – the finish line for the end of the chemo – just two hurdles, two more treatments to clear.

> Strange to say but the closer I got to that finish line, the less I focussed on it.

It had seemed so significant at the beginning but once I was within grasping distance, I almost felt indifferent to it.

As if that wasn't weird enough, I also felt guilty for feeling this way.

Even though I'd come so far, I felt like giving up.
I could see the finish line (like Stonehenge) – with family and friends gathered waiting
– but I felt no drive to get there anymore.
Charcoal drawing.

My Olympic Games

The Summer Olympics, which became known as London 2012, were fantastic, and gave the summer holiday a positive focus.

Watching athletes challenging their bodies and their minds, another reminder of the power of perseverance.

London 2012 ran its course – a tremendous feeling of pride seemed to waft across the country and everyone seemed to have enjoyed the positive and collective energy that had been triggered.

Coming to an end just before my 11th treatment, and so I was able to see my own finish line.

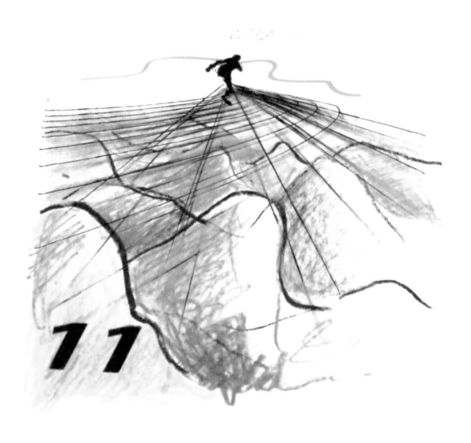

I couldn't help but see the connection between London 2012
and my own journey.
Pencils, pastels and computer.

A Different Me

It's funny but at the hospital I am always my official name although nobody calls me this, as I have had the nickname Gig since early childhood.

It's a strange feeling as they call my name or check my details – it's me but not me.

I quite liked this.

It was a way of holding this journey parallel with my own life and not allowing it to take over.

It was as if I became one person as I entered the hospital through those automatic revolving doors, and I left as another to carry on with my life.

The idea of keeping something back: I was one person outside the hospital and I became another when I passed through those big revolving doors.

The Yew Tree

I will always remember the mornings in 'the other house'; waking up to see the yew tree through the opened curtains. Twelve panes of glass in the white window frame, eight bigger at the bottom and four small at the top.

And I suddenly realised just how far I had come through my 12 Taxol treatments, with just one top pane to go.

I knew that I had been lucky, enduring the drugs well but I still craved freedom from the drugs, freedom from the sore veins, the dry mouth and the days when I was robbed of energy.

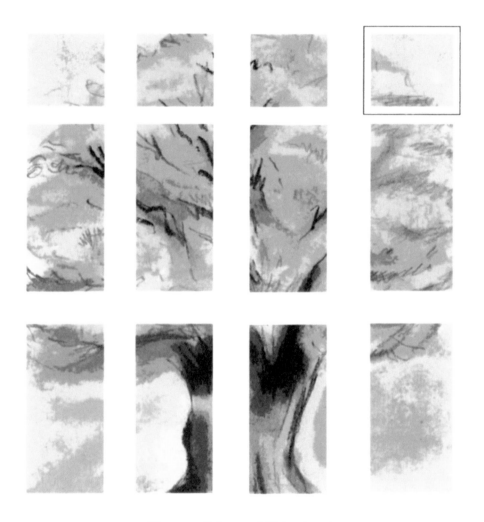

12 panes of glass and 12 treatments.
Staring out the window at the yew tree – from which Taxol is made.
I realised how far I had come.
Pastels, pencils and computer.

Lazy Summer Days

The girls waking up in their own sleepy time in the summer holidays was a wonderful time.

The first chatter between them, stifled by a yawn, footsteps to the bathroom toilet and the sound of a running tap if I was lucky (saving me the effort of prompting them to wash their hands).

And then, they'd appear beside me with fresh, big loving eyes anticipating the events of the day ahead.

Painting by Lulu.
This painting captures the magic of a rainbow, the sun shining,
a bird flying to its baby in the nest, the blue sky and flowers in bloom.
Perfect and precious.

The Last Chemo

I was really pensive leading up to my last treatment.

I felt emotionally flat - completely different to how I had expected I would feel.

It was a strange emotion and I almost felt guilty about the way I felt. It made me think about my dad who had his 80th birthday the following week. He would go through the motions of celebrating a landmark birthday but in reality not wanting to acknowledge it at all, given the choice. Why would he want to rejoice at being 80 when he'd sooner still be 60? My dad, the man who told his doctor, "Inside this fragile shell of a man, is Usain Bolt trying to get out!"

Healthwise, I was in fairly good shape considering. Actually I was 8lb more, rounded in shape and it wasn't good. It would have to go, when the time was right.

The treatment went like clockwork. I felt a subtle sense of achievement and wondered if it had served its purpose. I felt tired afterwards, and wondered if my body had reached its chemo-climax.

After a few embraces with staff, we headed for home collecting the girls from friends on route. My five-year-old was writing the alphabet onto a white board that evening, and although I was trying to help her, I kept getting letters muddled up. I was horrified the following morning when I felt fresh, to think that I hadn't been able to perform this simple task.

I felt no big crescendo at reaching my last chemo –
it just happened and was done.
Lost.
Painting and computer.

Post - chemo

In hindsight, The chemo sessions were far more daunting in my mind than they were in reality.

There were undoubtedly some rotten side-effects and days best forgotten. I became quite clumsy over the few weeks following my last chemo. The tips of my fingers were sore and I started to drop things.

I had also fallen over twice, one time taking my daughter down with me and grazing her wrist. I was achy and started to have hot flushes which was almost certainly the menopause accelerated by the chemo drugs.

There were some nights that were insufferably hot but I convinced myself I was no different to everyone else playing hokey-cokey with their duvets!

I'm still not sure if the pre-chemo 'talk' was a good thing for me. I know there is a legal obligation to share information with patients and give them advice on the possible side effects of chemotherapy. How else would they weigh up the decision to go ahead with treatment? But I wonder in hindsight if I'd have fared better without knowing and just crossing each bridge as I reached it.

I was so fortunate to stay physically and mentally strong. It's worth remembering that people rarely get all the side effects, I didn't get too many.

And it's good to have diversions.

My daughters were mine and I wonder how I would have coped without them, with just my illness to focus on.
It would have consumed me.

I was so scared of the chemo and yet once it had started, I felt determined to factor it into my life without letting it rule me. I used the demands and rituals of family life as my diversion.

Marbling inks and computer

Back to the future

The girls went back to school and I had to face up to the final stage of my journey. A mastectomy and reconstruction.

Ian and I had meetings with the breast surgeon and my oncologist in the same visit. A bombardment of information later and we left the hospital with a decision to make.

An implant or a body tissue replacement?

The body tissue replacement included the option to get a tummy tuck thrown in for free. The down side of this was that astonishingly I didn't have enough surplus tissue in this area to meet the capacity required for two breasts. I offered the suggestion of my buttocks to replenish the shortfall but apparently that wasn't going to be an option!

Time rolled on and my energy levels improved gradually and the fog lifted. I had six weeks before the operation so plenty of time to think it through. It was great to be free from the weekly visits for treatments and blood tests. I worked out that we'd travelled about 800 miles to and from the hospital.

Slowly but slowly my hair started to sprout again. One daughter said it was blonde-white, the other said black; in the end they decided that I was turning into a zebra which they were thrilled about (and it explained my weight gain).

I still had some bad days – days when I felt like screaming because the hot flushes were unbearable. I was prescribed some medication, anti-depressants actually, for people like me who cannot have the usual hormone replacement medication, and after a couple of weeks, I felt the benefit of these.

And I had days when I was scared because I wasn't having the treatments, the regular assurances.

It was a good two months before I felt really good again. My energy levels were fantastic and I realised just how far I had drifted from reality when I was on the chemo drugs.

Painting by Anna.
The power of a child's imagination is such a wonderful thing.
She's put her initial in the sun.
My girls were my sunshine throughout.

Lost and Found

The day arrived for my double mastectomy and reconstruction.

I waved the girls off to school – their day ahead familiar and safe – whilst mine was about as unfamiliar and daunting as I could imagine.

I gave my mum a huge hug (the sort that leave you with a sore throat) and off we went.

The operation was not nearly as uncomfortable as I had imagined. (Nothing like as painful as after a C-section). At 6.30 the following morning after surgery, I had been to the bathroom (which admittedly I was right next to) I had washed, dressed and was sat reading by the time the doctors did their morning rounds.

I felt like doing a victory lap to be this side of the op!

Wearing the drains for a few days afterwards was a bit awkward and heavy as I continued to lose blood after the surgery, which was quite normal, and they didn't look great so we decided not to bring the girls in to visit me in case they found it upsetting. For that reason, the Monday to Friday was a long haul and I missed them terribly. Friday finally came and I said my goodbyes to the other ladies in the ward of six.

The bonds of the hospital ward are special and true. They may be short-lived but they are deep. All walks of life thrown together with the common denominators of illness, anxiety and fear.

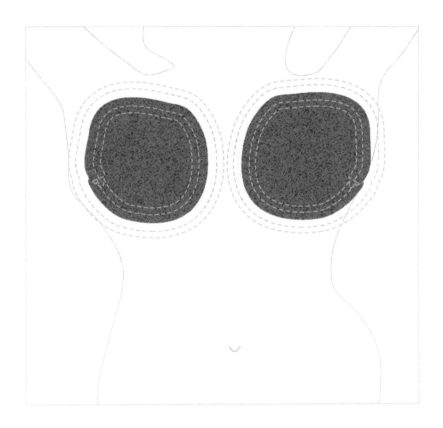

I was lucky enough to have two surgeons working on me in theatre – to minimise my time under anaesthetic. A double mastectomy and reconstruction at the same time. I went into theatre with breasts and I emerged with breasts.
Created on computer.

What's in a NAME?

I do believe in sheer coincidence, but sometimes I think coincidences are orchestrated by something much deeper than 'chance'.

The first coincidence was when the nurse arrived to complete my pre-surgery paperwork and had introduced herself as Florence. (No, I'm not going to suggest she was Florence Nightingale re-born!) Much simpler than that was the fact that the previous evening, I had suddenly declared to my mum (quite out of the blue) that I really like the name Florence.

The second coincidence was when the anaesthetist introduced himself as Louis, the male version of my daughter Louisa's name. We talked about spellings of names and he explained that he had the Spanish spelling Luis – which was even more weird because Louisa had just told me that she was going to start spelling her name without an 'o' as Luisa!

The last of the coincidences came later when I was stowed back in my ward recovering after four hours in theatre. I was lying listening to the sounds all around me, the other patients and the nurses milling around busily. And then, one nurse was calling another, "Gloria! Gloria!" and I just couldn't help smiling to myself. Ian had been talking just the day before, about names, and how some names beckon you to pronounce them in a particular accent. He's a little eccentric at times and has an imaginative mind, and after a few examples of 'James' versus 'Jimmy' and 'Vincent' versus 'Vinnie' (in all manner of accents) he settled on Gloria as an example of a name you don't hear very often.

All these thoughts made me smile and for reasons I cannot begin to explain, I felt pretty sure that I was going to be OK.

I'd had my three moments –
one before my op, one as I went
into theatre, and one back in
the ward afterwards.

I felt as though something or someone beyond this world was looking after me
throughout my surgery. The 'coincidences' of the names were signals
to make me feel safe.
Created on computer from a hand drawn sketch.

One nipple.

Obviously, I was quite bruised when the dressing was removed after my op. I tried to avoid letting the girls see me undressed until the bruises had faded but Lulu burst into the bathroom one day and apart from being a little surprised by the bruising, she was puzzled by the fact that I only had one nipple.

My left nipple, as predicted, had to be removed.

I hadn't really prepared for this moment and so when she asked me where my nipple was, I simply told her that because it was near to the 'hurty', the doctor had to take it.

"Take it where?" she asked.

She was pretty cross, telling me that I was to tell the doctor to give it back!

Words from a little girl intent on protecting her mummy.
It was only much later that I couldn't help seeing the funny side
of this scenario.

"Home Sweet Home"

I started sorting in the house – for our move back home. Whilst I padded up and down the stairs, I remembered how much of an ordeal going upstairs was for me during those summer months, when I'd have to rest after doing it just once. We'd been away from our house for over eight months.

How much had been endured within a year – how much had been achieved.

In the space of one year, we, as a family, had moved house and back again, I'd had 15 chemo treatments, about 30 blood tests, numerous scans, about 8 appointments in clinic – not to mention wig-fitting appointments and even a beauty therapy session! The way my eyebrows were growing, I could feel another beauty session coming along!

The move back home was intense but rewarding. Christmas was simple and precious, and I felt really focussed as the new year chimed its arrival.

I still had Herceptin treatments every three weeks, and then the ongoing Tamoxifen hormone treatment, but essentially, I felt free to live my life again.

Drawing with stickers by Lulu.
The simple joy of being back in our house for Christmas.
The irony of the pink ribbon sticker.

The End of the Line

My last Herceptin treatment was on 8th May – just before my eldest daughter was nine.

A landmark event that arrived quietly with no flags hoisted, just the usual friendly banter in the chemo suite, which would continue after I'd left.

A few warm embraces and a few thank you gifts passed to staff, and my journey was over where others were still mid-flow.

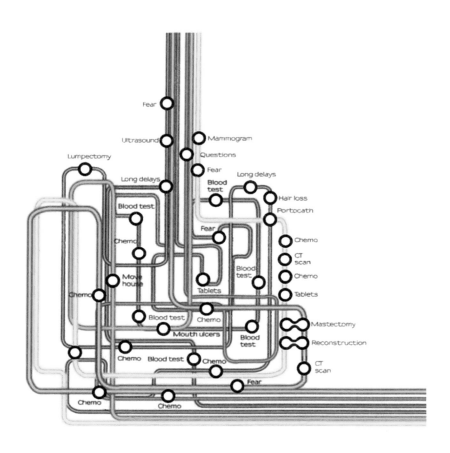

I'd reached the end of the line and was able to see the journey I'd made like a tube map of veins, with its many stops and starts, and its changing directions.

Created on computer.

Always one more Hurdle

I received a letter from the Genetics clinic.

The final hurdle that needed to be cleared, that affected my daughters, my nieces and even my brother and his son, I was told.

The meeting was short and sweet and I was told that my blood DNA needed to be analysed for any variants to the BRCA1 or BRCA2 genes.

Depending on the outcome of this result, the future for my children and my brother's all hung in the balance.

When the result finally arrived by post, I opened it without realising what it was and practically collapsed with relief to see that the report was negative.

The blood screening process was the final hurdle.
The blood creature in red ink – friend or foe?
Charcoal and ink drawing, distorted on computer.

Just one more thing...

Life gradually meandered back to normal consumed by the daily rituals, school runs, after school clubs and work.

The very final hurdle was the removal of my Portacath which happened four months after my last Herceptin treatment. The end of the Portacath, the end of the three weekly visits to get it flushed through with saline. A link, a bond severed and set free like an umbilical cord being cut.

I relished the simple things in life as if I'd been blind to them before.

I'd grabbed back my life, but it was more special, more happy, more fragile and precious than I had ever realised.

I cherished the way that my daughter took a deep breath when she was reading aloud to me, to indicate a full stop; I cherished the sound of them both glugging when they were thirstily drinking, and I cherished the way that when they learned something new, they would tell us with such excitement as if we too were learning it for the first time.

I took this photo on a boat trip years ago. It summed up the freedom that I felt once the Portacath had been removed.

Happiness!

Sometime much later, I was painting with my oldest daughter and we were squeezing tubes of acrylic paint onto a palette.

We both knew that if her younger sister appeared as we were squeezing one particular tube, that she would be in fits of laughter.

Moments later she did appear, curious to see what we were doing, and seeing the big blob of brown paint she dissolved into laughter saying:

"Poooooo, pooooooo."

Happiness...is knowing how your daughter will react
when she sees the blob of fresh brown paint.